Contents

Edited by Anne Linehan and Laura Woodard
Illustrations by Linda Starr

Published by Teaching Resource Center
P.O. Box 82777, San Diego, CA 92138

Introduction

Learning Letters with Mixed Fonts will provide students with opportunities to carefully examine the letters of the alphabet. As they sort the letters and play the games, students will discover consistencies that will help them independently recognize and name the letters and know the sounds they make, which is the basis for phonemic awareness.

To begin, discuss the visual characteristics of the letters:

What is their shape, their size, their length?
Do they have horizontal, vertical, diagonal, or
 curving lines?
Do parts of the letter extend above or below a
 base line?
Do they have circles or tunnels?
Do they have a line that crosses through them?
Do they have tails, dots, or curves?

Comparing fonts can establish that even when letters come in different sizes and styles, you can still recognize them by their special features. These experiences, followed by one of the following activities, will help children make the connections needed for beginning alphabet recognition.

Learning Letters with Mixed Fonts provides you with two sizes of lowercase and uppercase letters. The small letters are in fifteen different fonts. The larger card-size set has four different fonts. Prepare the letters for the suggested activities and games ahead of time. Make copies of the letters before cutting them apart. You may want to copy the letters onto card stock to make them sturdy enough for repeated use. Use resealable bags or envelopes for organizing and storing the letters.

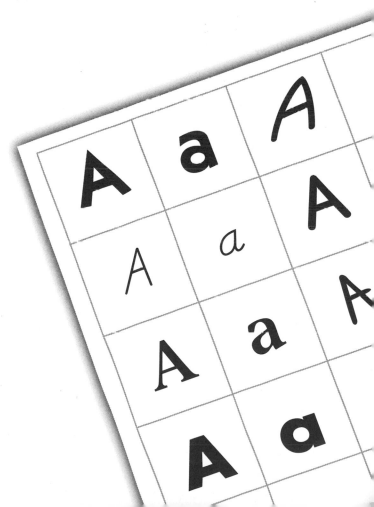

Sorting with Learning Letters

Sorting and matching are favorite activities of children. Using the small letters in this book to sort and match upper and lowercase forms in a variety of fonts will help students learn the features of each letter.

We suggest that you begin with the letters b, m, r, and s. Follow with these other groupings: (t, g, n, p) (c, h, f, d) (l, k, j, w) (y, z, v, q). These clusters are arranged according to 1) frequency of occurrence and 2) familiar sound and shape distinction. Have the children sort two letters at a time in the early stages, increasing the number as they gain mastery.

Management tip: Use a flat surface, sorting mat or blackline grid (page 63) for sorting the letters.

Sorts to Consider

• sort lowercase letters only
• sort uppercase letters only
• sort and match a variety of both uppercase and lowercase letters
• sort letters with tails
• sort letters with circles
• sort letters that are straight or tall or both
• sort letters that are round or short or both
• do "open sorts" where students determine their own categories
• sort beginning sounds to matching pictures
• sort the letters in alphabetical order

As children become more proficient in recognizing the letter features they may begin to discover familiar words in their sorts. Encourage this development by setting up letter sorts such as p, c, t, n, a. Provide opportunities for the student to make their own connections between the letter groups, letter-sound relationships and words.

Sorting by Color

Color-code sets of letters by copying them on colored paper. Example: one color for short, round letters, another color for straight, tall letters. Ask the students to sort by color. After the students have completed the sort, ask them what they think the colors mean.

Sorting with Category Cards

Make sorting category cards. Write one category per card. Use a different color pen to write each pair of sorting categories. Use the category cards to label different sorts.

uppercase	lowercase
tall	short
sticks	no sticks
round	not round
dot	no dot
tail	no tail
thin	thick
in my name	not in my name
slanted	straight

Activities & Games

Mystery Letter

Materials: various large letters
Players: 2 or more

Place the cards in a pile facedown on the table. The first player draws a card from the pile and keeps it from the view of the other players as s/he gives a verbal clue about the letter. The other players try to guess what the letter is. If they guess incorrectly, the player gives more clues until someone identifies the letter. Then the next player chooses a letter card, and so on.

Name Signs

Materials: grid paper
             pen or pencil
             small letters

Begin by using the students' first names to draw attention to the letter formations and characteristics. Have the children create "name signs." Pre-write each child's first name on grid paper, one letter to a square. (If two first names are alike, include initials for last names.) Place the letters on the table, out of order. Have the children select the letters to match the letters in their names.

Who Has It?

Materials: a picture card for each player
             large letter card to match each
                 picture's beginning sound
Players: 26 or less

Give each student one picture card and make sure s/he is familiar with its name. Hold up a letter card and ask, "Who Has It?" The child with the picture card that matches the letter says the letter name and comes up and takes the letter. After everyone has a letter, have the players line up in alphabetical order with their picture cards and letters.

Variation: match lowercase to uppercase letters.

Letter/Picture Chart

Materials: chart paper
             all large letters
             crayons and paper
             old magazines
             scissors
             glue

Use the large large letters to make a letter/picture chart for each of the twenty-six letters of the alphabet. Have students paste all eight different B's, for example, all over the chart and then draw or cut out and paste pictures that begin with that letter. Hang the chart on the wall. Use the chart to read the letter names and sounds either in alphabetical order or in a less structured way.

More **Activities**

Letter Patterns

Materials: large letter cards
pocket chart

Create letter patterns in the pocket chart using letters with similar (or different) visual characteristics, for example:

t l f t l f t l f t l f

v w x V W X v w x

m n u m n u

b p d q b p d q

C D G O Q

E F L H E F L H

A A V V A A V V

c C o O c C o O c C o O c C

W M W M W M W M

Z N Z N Z N Z N

The Alphabet Song

Materials: a set of large letters, A to Z
pocket chart
small letters, A to Z
2 sheets of grid paper (page 63)
taped together
glue
scissors
crayons

Use the large letters to lay out the alphabet song "lyrics." This will take eight rows in a pocket chart. Then have the class sing the song.

Next photocopy the grid blackline two times for each student. Tape two copies together to make ten rows, like the pocket chart. Let the students choose letters to build their own *Alphabet Song* on the grid. Using the pocket chart as a model, have them glue the letters to the squares. They can use crayons to color or make designs in the remaining blank squares.

Mixed Print Mini-Poster

Materials: photocopy of small letters
printed matter (cereal boxes, magazines, newspapers, fliers, lettering books, etc.)
scissors
glue
construction paper

Make a mini-poster with different print styles and sizes by cutting and pasting the small letters together with a variety of other print sources.

Alphabet Maze

Materials: small letters
             glue
             1 prepared grid sheet per student

Create a maze by gluing a variety of letter styles on the grid (page 63) using the model below. Make a copy for each student to solve by finding the path in alphabetical order.

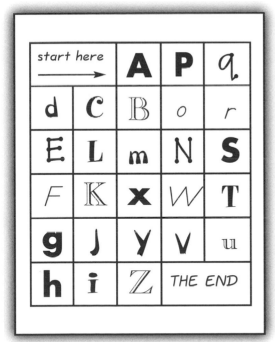

Remember the Letter
(Concentration)

Materials: pairs of matching letter cards
Players: 2 or more

Prepare sets of upper and lowercase letters that students need to practice. The sets can range from eight pairs (sixteen cards total) to twenty-six pairs (fifty-two cards total) depending on the abilities of the players.

Arrange the cards facedown in rows of four. The first player turns two cards face-up, keeping them in the same spots. If the two letters match, the player keeps the cards and continues with his/her turn. If the two letters do not match, the player turns them facedown and the next player takes a turn. The object is to see who can make the highest number of pairs by remembering where the cards were placed when turned over previously. The game is over when all the cards are matched.

Concentration Variations:
• Have the players match the pictures with their beginning sounds.
• Use one uppercase and one lowercase for each letter you want to study. Have the players match the lowercase with the uppercase letter.
• Have the players match the lowercase and uppercase by font, using all eight different cards for each letter. (Choose two letters for a sixteen card game; use more to make it harder.)

Word Building

Materials: divided letter storage boxes
             a selection of small letters
             paper
             glue

Select letters that will be easy for students to make words from, e.g., p, c, t, n, a. Guide the students in manipulating the letters to build words. At the end of the activity, have them glue a favorite word onto paper.

More Games

Old O

(Old Maid)

Materials: 26 pairs of letter cards (lowercase and uppercase)
1 "Old O" card

Players: 2 to 6

Mix up the cards. For two players, use only half the deck (thirteen two-card sets). Make sure you include the Old O card. Use the whole deck for three or more players.

Deal out the cards until none are left. It does not matter if one player gets more cards than the others. Players remove any matches from their hands and place them face-up in their own discard pile. The players then hold the remaining cards in their hands so only the backs can be seen. The players take turns picking a card from the hand of the player on the left. The object of the game is to get rid of all the cards in one's hand by making matches. When a match is made, the player puts it in his/her discard pile. The game continues until the only player left is the one holding the Old O card.

Go Read

(Go Fish)

Materials: 8 to 26 pairs of matching letter cards (depending on the number or players and their abilities)

Players: 2 or more

Each player gets five cards, and the rest go in a drawing pile in the middle. Each player may then remove any letter pairs in his/her hand and place them face-up in a discard pile. Player one may ask any other player for a letter card that matches one in his/her hand. For example, if player one has a T card, he asks player two if she has a T. If she does, she must give it to him. Player one places the pair face-up in the discard pile and continues asking other players for specific letters that match his. If she does not have the matching letter card, she says, "Go read!" Player one must then draw a card from the pile and his turn is finished. The game is over when one player is out of cards or when the drawing pile is gone. The player with the most pairs wins.

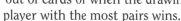

A	a	*A*	*a*	𝕬	𝖆
A	*a*	**A**	**a**	**A**	**a**
A	a	A	a	A	a
A	**a**	A	a	𝔄	a
A	Aa	Aa	Aa	A	a

B	b	*B*	*b*	𝕭	𝖇
B	*b*	**B**	**b**	**B**	**b**
B	**b**	B	b	B	b
B	**b**	B	b	*B*	b
B	**b**	**B**	b	B	b

C	c	C	c	C	c
C	c	C	c	C	C
C	C	C	c	C	C
C	c	C	C	C	c
C	c	C	c	C	C

D	d	D	d	D	d
D	d	D	d	D	d
D	d	D	d	D	d
D	d	D	d	D	d
D	d	D	d	D	d

E	e	E	e	E	e
E	e	E	e	E	e
E	e	E	e	E	e
E	e	E	e	E	e
E	e	E	e	E	e

G	g	G	g	G	g
G	g	G	g	G	g
G	g	G	g	G	g
G	g	G	g	G	g
G	g	G	g	G	g

H	h	H	h	H	h
H	h	H	h	H	h
H	h	H	h	H	h
H	h	H	h	H	h
H	h	H	h	H	h

I	i	/	i	I	í
I	i	I	i	I	i
I	i	l	i	l	i
I	i	l	i	l	í
I	i	l	i	I	i

J	j	J	j	J	j
J	j	J	j	J	j
J	j	J	j	J	j
J	i	J	j	J	j
J	j	J	i	J	j

K	k	K	k	K	k
K	k	K	k	K	k
K	k	K	k	K	k
K	k	K	k	K	k
K	k	K	k	K	k

L	I	L	I	L	L
L	l	L	I	L	I
L	1	L	I	L	I
L	I	L	I	L	I
L	1	L	I	L	1

M	m	M	m	M	m
M	m	M	m	M	m
M	m	M	m	M	m
M	m	M	m	M	m
M	m	M	m	M	m

N	n	N	n	N	n
N	n	N	n	N	n
N	n	N	n	N	n
N	n	N	n	N	n
N	n	N	n	N	n

P	p	*P*	*p*	𝔓	𝔭
P	*p*	P	p	**P**	P
P	p	p	p	p	p
P	**p**	P	p	*P*	p
P	p	P	þ	P	p

Q	q	Q	q	Q	q
Q	q	Q	q	Q	q
Q	q	Q	q	Q	q
Q	q	Q	q	Q	q
Q	q	Q	q	Q	q

R	r	R	r	R	r
R	r	R	r	R	r
R	r	R	r	R	r
R	r	R	r	R	r
R	r	R	r	R	r

S	S	S	S	S	S
S	S	S	S	S	S
S	S	S	S	S	S
S	S	S	S	S	S
S	S	S	S	S	S

T	T t	T	t	T	t
T	t	T	t	T	t
T	t	T	t	T	t
T	t	T	t	t	t
T	T t	T	t	T	t

U	u	U	u	U	u
U	u	U	u	**U**	u
U	u	U	u	U	u
U	u	U	u	U	u
U	u	U	u	U	u

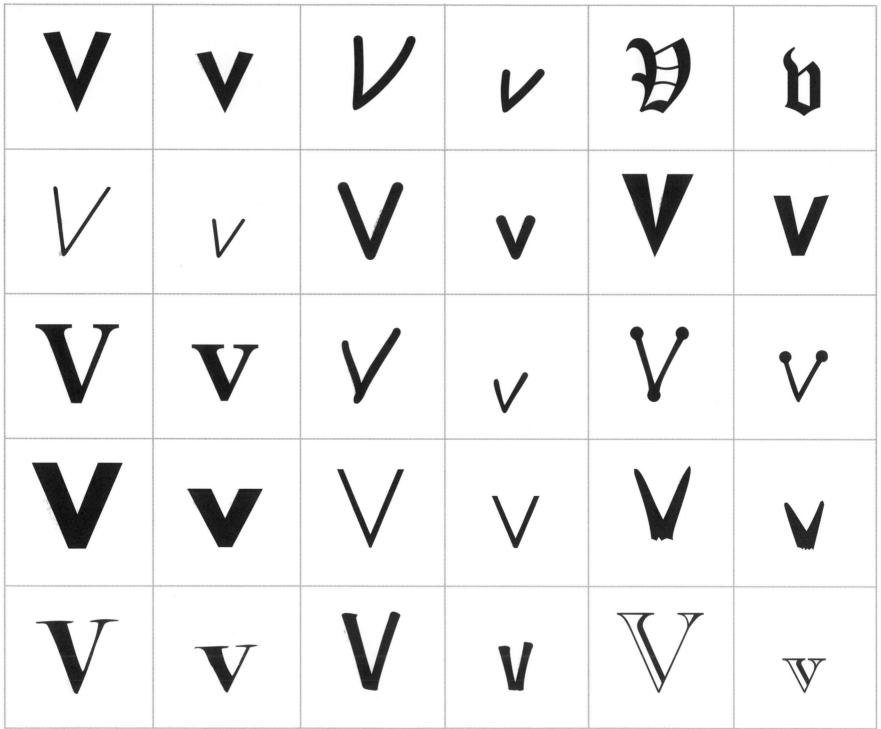

W	**w**	*W*	*w*	𝖂	𝖜
W	ɯ	**W**	**w**	**W**	**W**
W	**w**	W	w	W	W
W	**w**	W	W	W	w
W	w	**W**	**w**	W	W

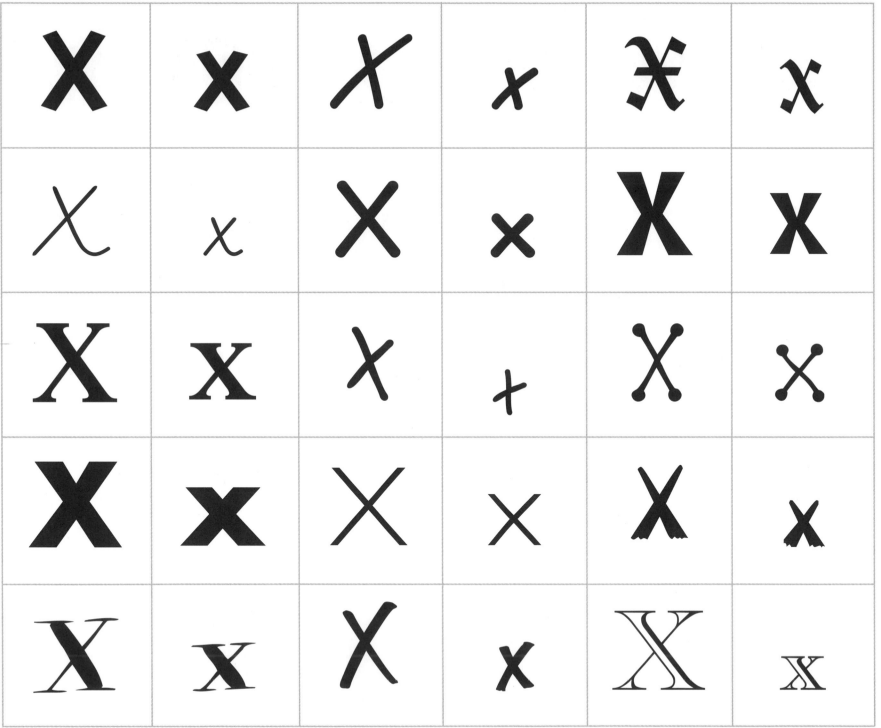

Y	y	Y	y	Y	y
Y	y	Y	Y	Y	Y
Y	y	Y	Y	Y	y
Y	y	Y	y	Y	y
Y	y	Y	y	Y	y

Z	z	Z	z	Z	ʒ
Z	z	Z	z	**Z**	**Z**
Z	z	Z	z	Z	z
Z	**z**	Z	z	Z	z
Z	z	Z	z	Z	z

B B B B

b b b b

C C C C

c c c c

D D D D

d d d d

36

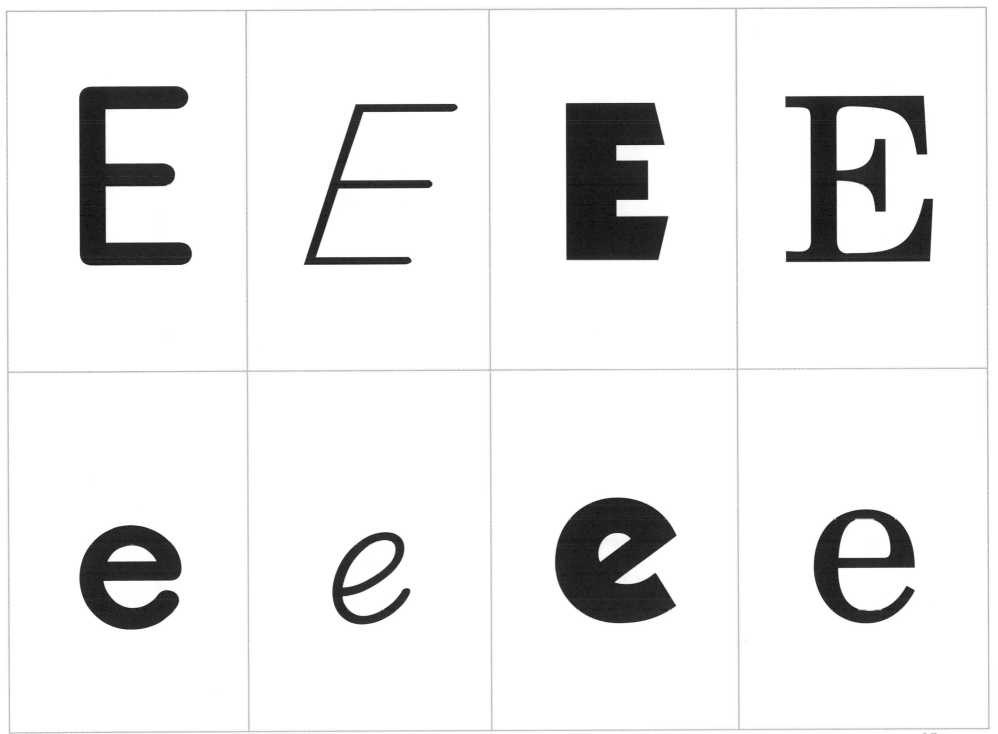

F F F F

f f f f

G   G   G   G

g   g   g   g

H H **H** H

h h **h** h

40

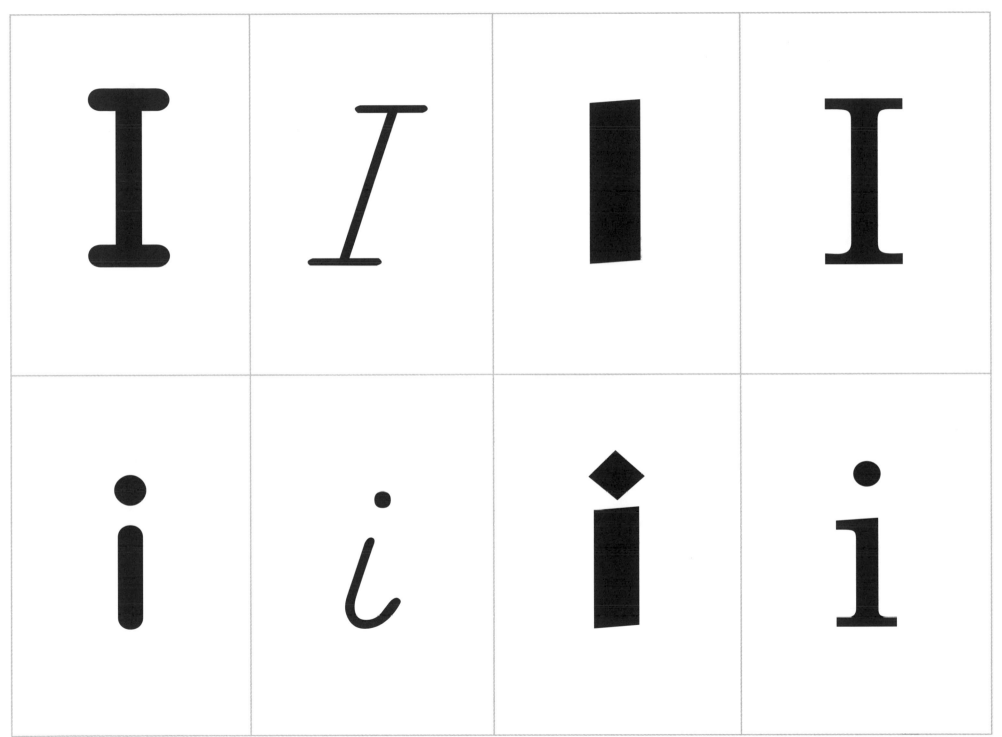

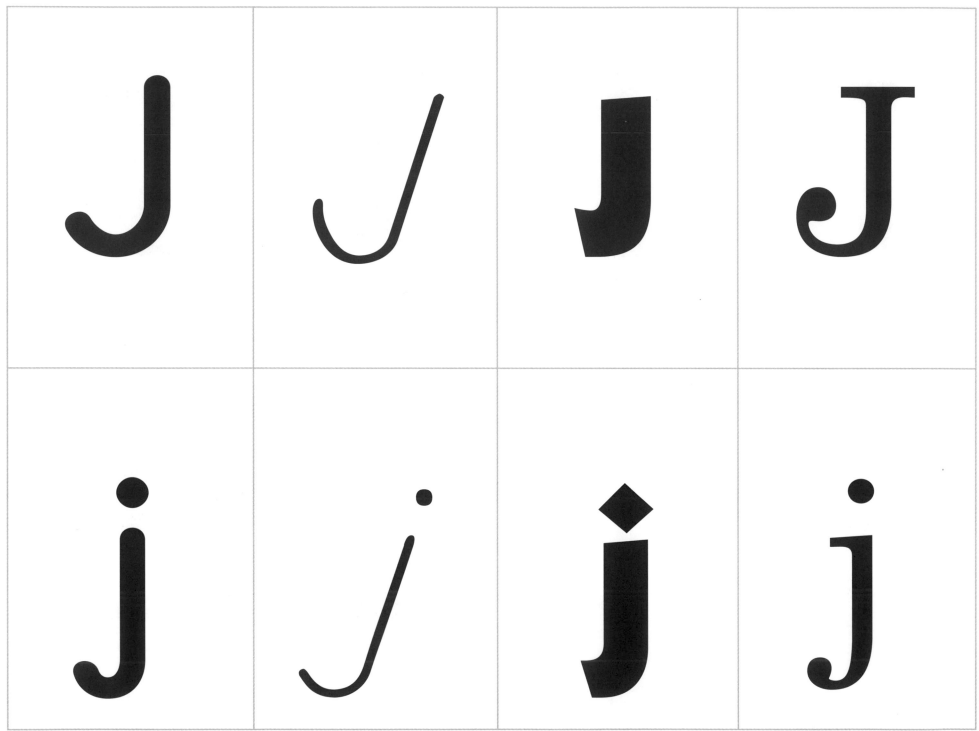

K K **K** K

k k **k** k

L L L L

l l l 1

M M **M** M

m m **m** m

N N N N

n n n n

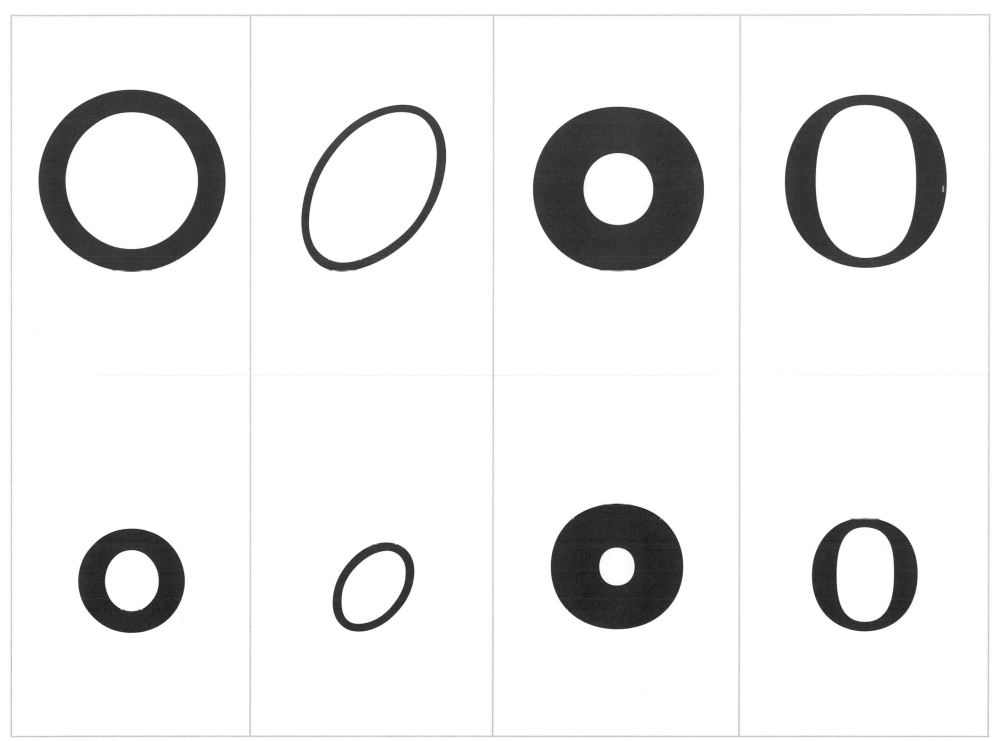

P p **P** P

p p **p** p

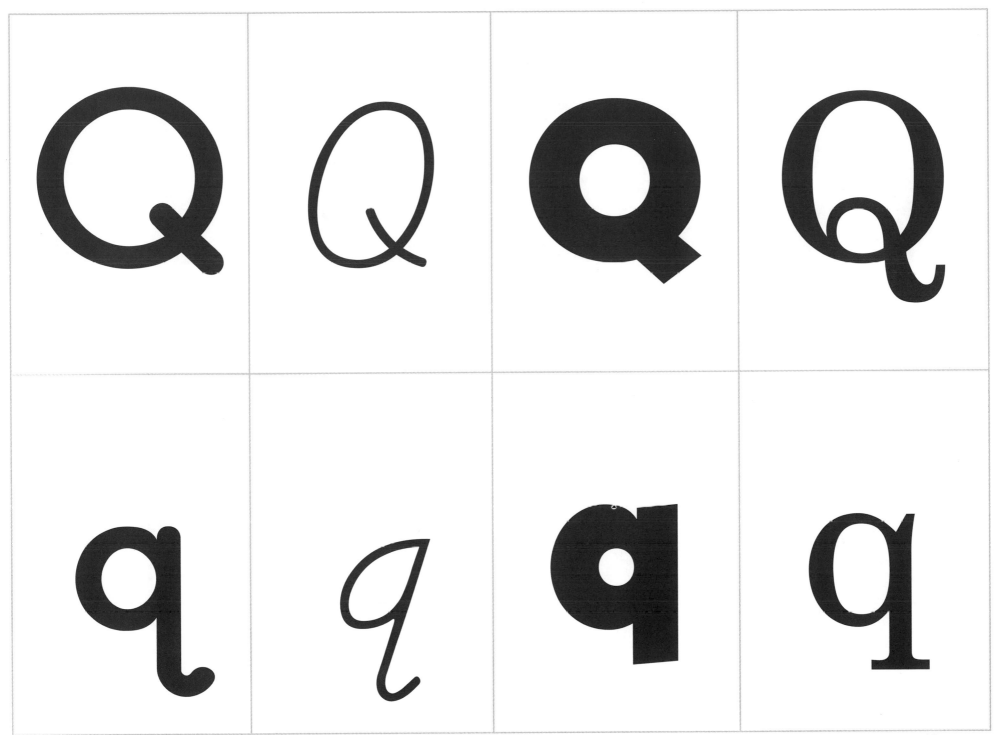

R   ℛ   **R**   R

r   r   **r**   r

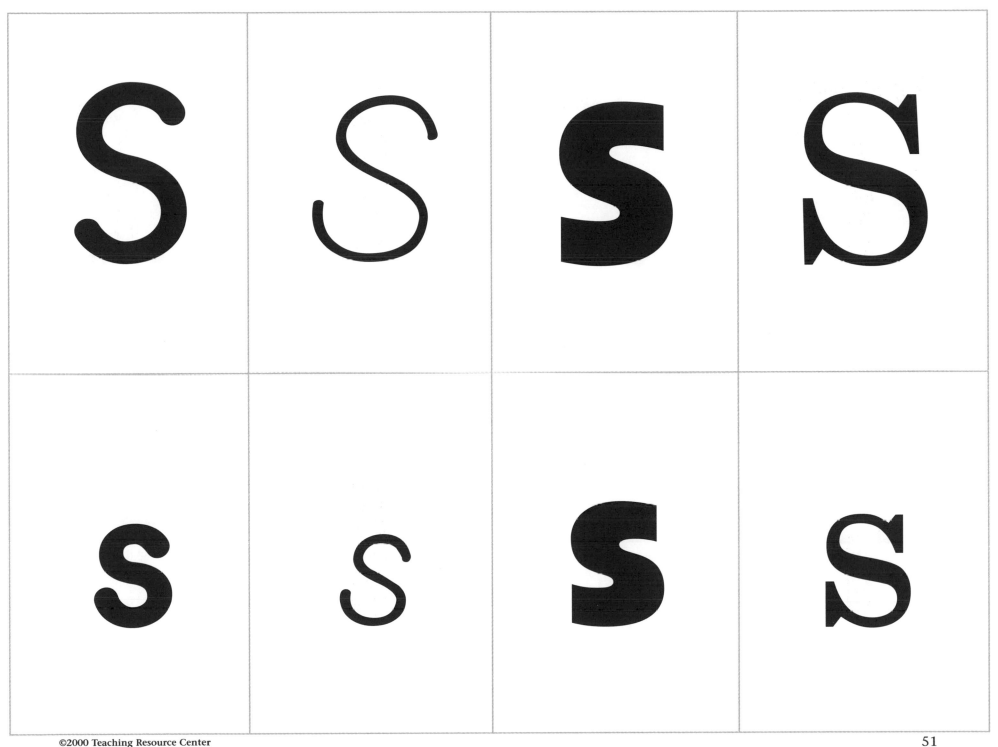

T T T T

t t t t

u u u U

u u u u

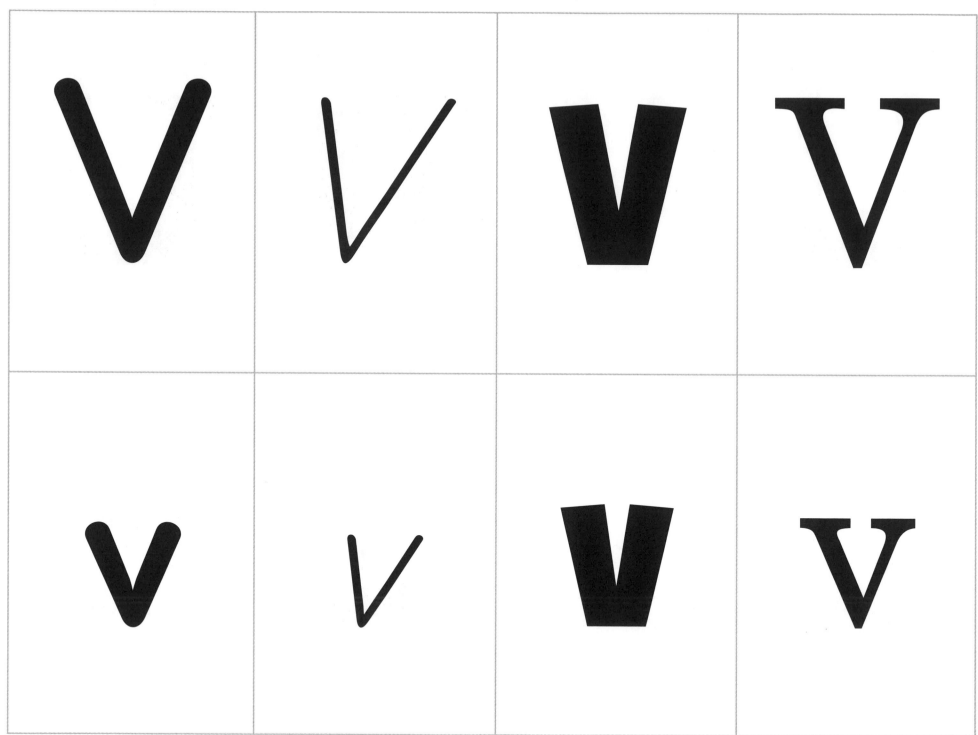

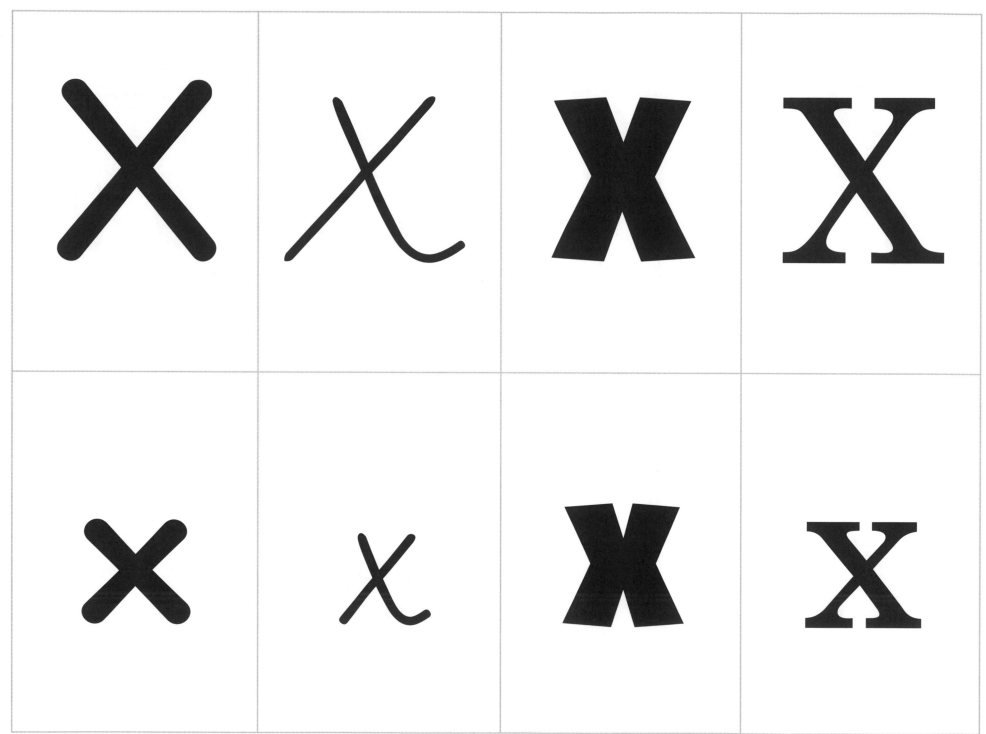

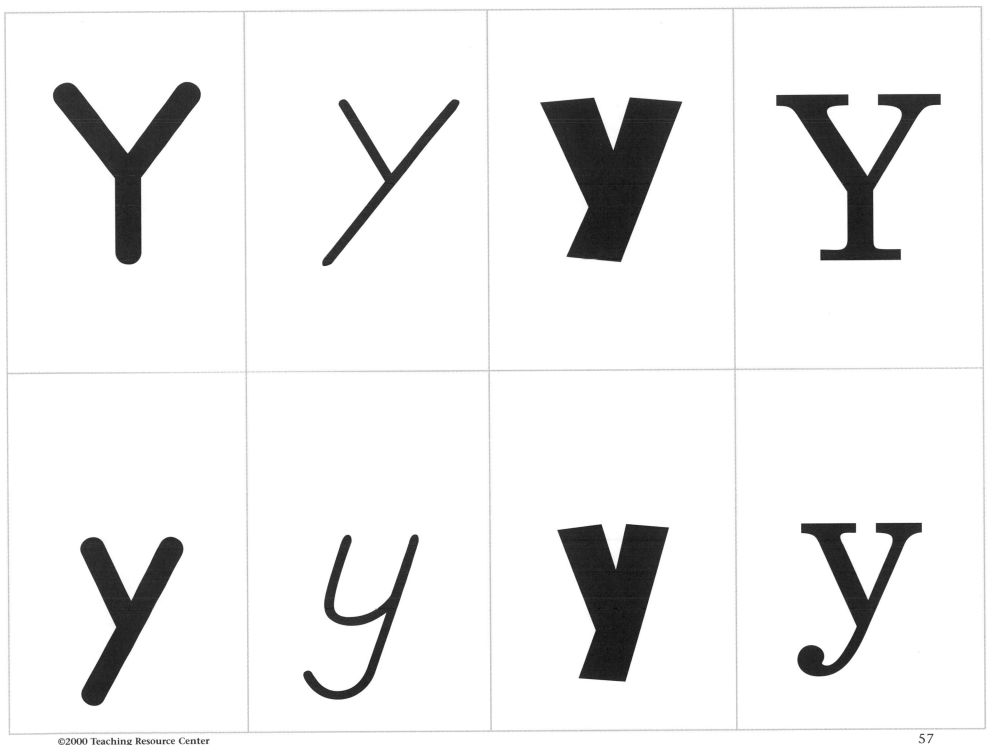

Z Z Z Z

Z Z Z Z

OLD

Related Resource Materials

Alphabet Linking Poster
Alphabet Linking Tent
Alphabet Matching Puzzles
Avalanche of Letters
Beaded Alphabet Cards
Beginning Sound Sort Cards
Blacklines for Letter Formation
Giant Alphabet Cards
Lauri Alphabet Puzzles
Magnetic Foam Letters
Rubber Stamp Alphabet
Tactile Letters
Trace 'n Erase

Storage

Letter Storage Boxes
Storage Pouches, velcro & magnetic
Translucent Plastic Folders, Bags & Files
Wooden Alphabet Sorting Box

Books

Alphabet Mini-Books
    by Anne Linehan
Guided Reading: Good First Teaching for All Children
    by Irene Fountas & Gay Su Pinnell
Implementing the 4-Blocks Literacy Model
    by Cheryl Mahaffey Sigmon
Making Big Words
    by Patricia M. Cunningham & Dorothy P. Hall
Making Words
    by Patricia M. Cunningham & Dorothy P. Hall
Month-by-Month Reading and Writing for Kindergarten
    by Patricia M. Cunningham & Dorothy P. Hall
Phonics from A to Z: A Practical Guide
    by Wiley Blevins
Tangram Alphabet
    by Anne Linehan & Janis Poe
Word Matters: Teaching Phonics and Spelling in the Reading/Writing Classroom
    by Irene Fountas & Gay Su Pinnell
Words Their Way, 2nd Edition
    by Donald Bear, et al.

All of these resources are available from Teaching Resource Center

Call 1-800-833-3389 for a free catalog or find us online at www.trcabc.com